# ROCK ON!

## Contents

Diana Bentley

Story illustrated by
Steve May

Heinemann

## Find out about

• All sorts of weird instruments

## Tricky words

• music
• musical
• instrument
• steel drum
• skatar
• boghorn

Introduce these tricky words and help the reader when they come across them later!

## Text starter

You can make music with lots of things. You can make music with a steel drum or even a skateboard or a saw. But there's one more amazing thing you can make music with!

# Weird Instruments

You can make music
with lots of things.

Is this a musical instrument?

Yes it is!
It is a steel drum.

You can make music with it.

Is this a musical instrument?

Yes it is!
It is a skatar.

It is made from a skateboard and a guitar.

You can make music with it.

Is this a musical instrument?

Yes it is!
It is a saw.

You can make music with it.

Is this a musical instrument?

Yes it is!
It is a boghorn.

## Text Detective

- How do people make music with a saw?
- Would you like to play a boghorn? Why?

## Word Detective

- Phonic Focus: Initial phonemes

  Page 4: Find a word beginning with the phoneme 'd'.
- Page 4: Why is there an exclamation mark at the end of the sentence?
- Page 4: How many syllables (beats) are there in the word 'musical'?

## Super Speller

Read these words:

### do   by

Now try to spell them!

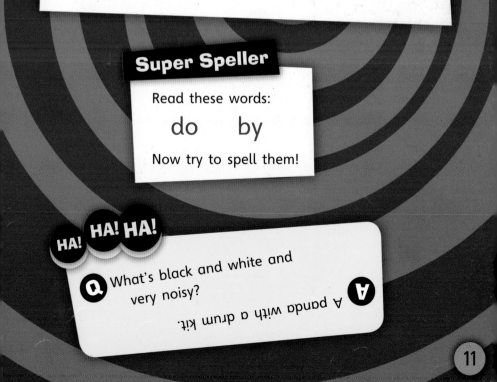

HA! HA! HA!

**Q** What's black and white and very noisy?

**A** A panda with a drum kit.

## In this story

Lee

Emma

## Tricky words

- guitar
- keyboard
- drums

Introduce these tricky words and help the reader when they come across them later!

## Story starter

Lee and Emma are twins. They are great friends but one twin is always trying to be better than the other twin. One day, Lee was practising with his band. Emma wanted to play in the band.

# The School Band

"Can I play in the band?"
said Emma.

"Yes," said Lee.
"What can you play?"

Do you think Emma will be good at playing the guitar?

"I can play the guitar," said Emma.

"No," said Lee.
"You are no good."

"I can play the keyboard,"
said Emma.

"No," said Lee.
"You are no good."

"I can play the drums,"
said Emma.

"No, no, no!" said Lee.

"Can I sing in the band?"
said Emma.

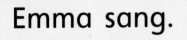

Emma sang.

"You are good," said Lee.
"You can sing in the band!"

# Quiz

Text Detective

- Why did Lee let Emma join the band?
- If you were in a band would you like to play an instrument, sing or both?

## Word Detective

- **Phonic Focus:** Initial phonemes
  Page 14: Find a word beginning with the phoneme 'p'.
- Page 13: Find two little words inside the word 'band'.
- Page 16: Find a word that rhymes with 'hood'.

## Super Speller

Read these words:

### in    he

Now try to spell them!

**HA! HA! HA!**

**Q** Why did grandma put wheels on her rocking chair?

**A** So she could rock 'n' roll.

24